Withdrawn from Stock

D0335880

This book belongs to..

....

To read with..

To Andrew, Catherine and Flora – E.U.

For all the little victims of the dreaded scritchy-scratchy beastie,
you have my sympathies – S.H.

RED SQUIRREL BOOKS

Published in 2014 in Great Britain by Barrington Stoke Ltd
18 Walker Street, Edinburgh, EH3 7LP

www.redsquirrelbooks.co.uk

This story was first published in a different form in *Wow! 366*, Scholastic Children's Books, 2008

Text © 2008 Eleanor Updale
Illustrations © 2014 Sarah Horne

The moral right of Eleanor Updale and Sarah Horne to be identified as the author and illustrator of
this work has been asserted in accordance with the Copyright, Designs and Patents Act, 1988

All rights reserved. No part of this publication may be reproduced in whole or in any part in any form
without the written permission of the publisher

A CIP catalogue record for this book is available from the British Library upon request

ISBN 978-1-78112-294-5

Printed in China by Toppan Leefung PTE. Ltd

Eleanor Updale and Sarah Horne

Itch Scritch
Scratch

RED SQUIRREL BOOKS

I have a lot of little friends,

Who live upon my head.

They jog and jive and jiggle

When I am in my bed.

Withdrawn from Stock
Dublin City Public Libraries

And then, when I am fast asleep,

Their wives start laying eggs.

Each egg contains a little louse,

With lots of little legs.

He had six legs with evil claws

To cling onto my hair,

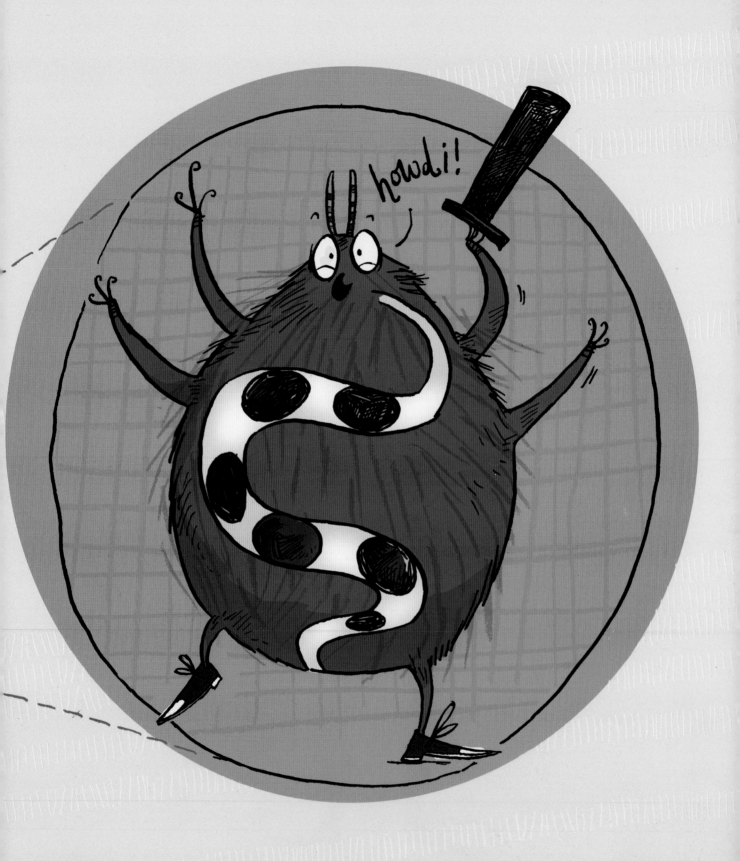

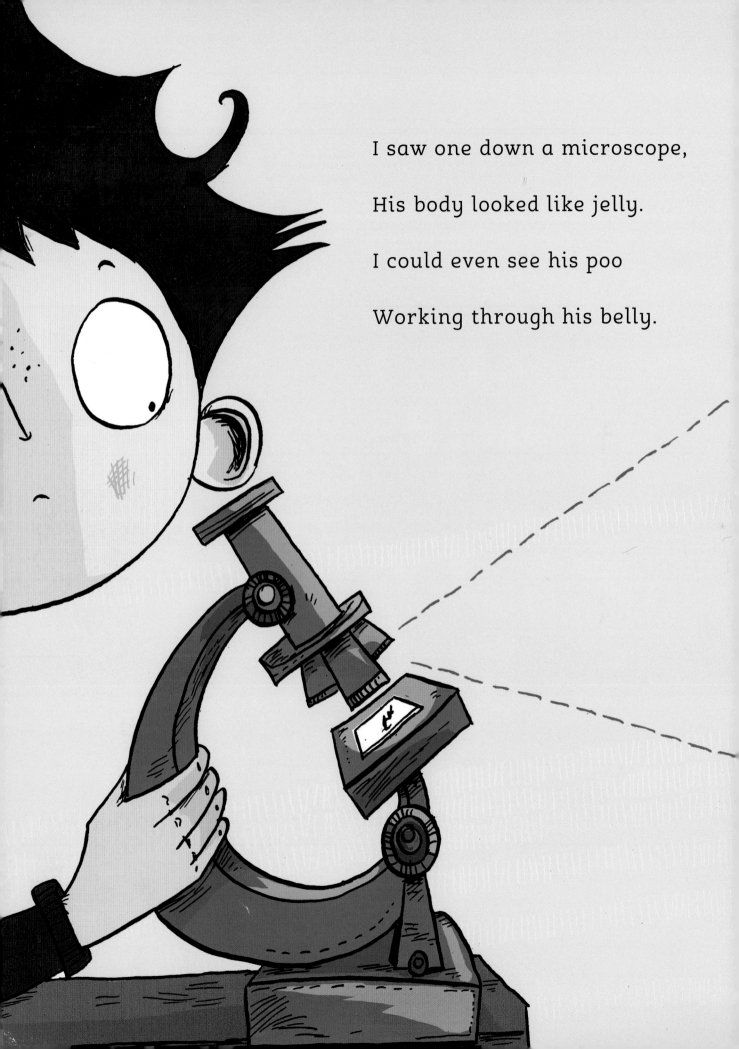

I saw one down a microscope,

His body looked like jelly.

I could even see his poo

Working through his belly.

And two short pointy aerials

That he waved in the air.

Aerials
x2
(pointy)

Claws
x6 (evil)

Legs x6
(wiggly)

curly-Toed
dancing shoes

Extraordinary
Stripy socks

Lice don't make any honey,

They don't spin any thread,

You can't sell them for money,

You can't eat them with bread.

To my mind, lice are useless,

And it's worse than you expected.

They make you itch, they make you scratch,

Those bites can get infected!

My mum went mad with chemicals,

With shampoo and a comb,

Till yells and screams of agony

Rang from our happy home.

My sister, who has longer hair,

Could only scream and shout,

As my mum brushed and combed and tugged,

To get the head lice out.

They cursed, they swore, they hoovered us,

To get the lice away.

My mum tried everything she could,

And so did other mummies.

But all their eggs were stuck with glue

Extruded from their tummies.

But those bugs just kept on laying eggs,

To hatch another day.

Each lady louse lays 83,

And each of them lays more.

There really is no way that we

Can hope to win this war.

But it's not all bad. Just think of this –

In one way they're quite cool.

'Cause if you show the teachers them,

You get the day off school.

NOW P

ST

SCRAT

LEASE OP CHING!

Leabharlanna Poibli Chathair Baile Átha Cliath

Dublin City Public Libraries

Grow a love of reading

RED SQUIRREL BOOKS